Rescue!

Written by Jane Langford

Illustrated by Colin H. Paine

Tom and Jamie were fishing in some rock pools. Jamie saw the huge wave coming towards them, but Tom was looking at a crab...

The wave washed Tom over the edge
of the rock and into the sea below.

Jamie screamed for help, and Tom's dad rushed over at once.

He fell in the sea! Where's he gone? I can't see him!

5

Tom's dad plunged into the sea, but he couldn't see a thing. He put his head under the water to look, but a wave dragged him through a gap in the rocks. The sea sucked him up and spat him into a cave.

I can't see Tom's dad.

Dad looked around the cave. It was dark, but not empty. There was something moving at the back. It was Tom.

The coastguard rescue boat came to where Jamie was marking the spot. Jamie told them that Tom and his dad had been washed away. The crew knew there was a cave in the rocks.

11

The diver swam through the gap into the cave, and tied the rope to a rock. Tom went out first.

At last Tom and Dad were out of the cave. Their heads bobbed up out of the water and they saw the lifeboat.

15

The boat took them safely back to Mum and Jamie. On the beach, they all hugged each other.